W9-BXY-828

Dedication

With love, I dedicate this book to Our Lady of Fatima and also to my earthly mother, Dorothy Elizabeth Kranz, "Great Grandma" to many. Thank you for helping me to know the love of Jesus and Mary.

Important Word Meanings

Catechism - What the Catholic Church teaches.

Sacrifice - Doing something hard out of love for God.

Impressed – Special thoughts about someone or something.

Pride – Thinking too much of how others see us.

Inspired - When God nudges us to do something good.

Vanity - Thinking too much about looking pretty.

Offer up - When we offer to God as a prayer, the hard things in life   knowing Our Lady will use the graces for great good.

Conversion - When someone turns to God.

Scapular - Worn over the shoulders, it is a sign of our love of The Blessed Mother. God blesses it to protect us from harm and help save our souls.

Immaculate Heart - Mary's heart is totally pure and beats only with love for God and all of us!

Jacinta is soon to receive her First Holy Communion. She has learned her *catechism* lessons in her mind but not yet fully in her heart. Her mother has decided to make a dress for her little one, *sacrificing* her own wedding gown and knows just what she'll say as she presents it! When that day finally comes, she tells her young daughter…

I've made your First Communion dress
It's satin and oh so dear
The fabric from my wedding gown
I saved through all the years

I knew that we could not afford
A brand new dress of lace
So I cut into my own gown
And made it, by God's grace

I worked so hard to make it
Every stitch with love for you
To make you feel special
And very happy too

Jacinta looks at the dress with a very sad frown, for she wants an extra fancy one, with lots of ruffles, ribbon and such! She takes it from her mother but tears begin to flow down her face as she cries...

Mama I know you meant well

But I don't like this dress

It isn't pretty with lots of frills

Like Lisa's Amy's or Tess

I want to look like a princess

On my First Communion Day

So everyone will be impressed

And sure to look my way

Jacinta doesn't even seem to notice how her words hurt her mother, who was so excited to make her little girl happy!   Out of *pride*, she is only thinking of herself.

Now her mother feels like crying but instead, kneels in front of the statue of Our Lady of Fatima and prays the holy Rosary. She asks The Blessed Mother to pray for her little girl, to see what is most important. Soon, she is *inspired* to tell Jacinta a story...

Years ago a communion veil

Was worn by my grandmother

It was truly special

Unlike any other

As you were getting near in age

She wanted you to have it

The only thing, my little one

She forgot just where she put it

So let us ask Our Lady's help

This veil will soon appear

And you will feel so happy

When you wear it, daughter dear

Suddenly a big smile spreads across Jacinta's face. She is thinking of the treasure hunt she will have, looking for the veil, for they have just moved to Great Grandmother's house where she had lived all her life. Jacinta thinks that if she has this veil, she will look the prettiest of all the girls so, in *vanity* she prays...

Dear God, I need a miracle

Please help me to discover

Where is the First Communion Veil

Once worn by Great Grandmother

I will look in ever closet

In every cabinet door

If I don't find it here today

Next day I'll look some more

After a few days, Jacinta has still not found the veil. She has looked in every place she can think of...even under the beds and complains to her mother, "Maybe I'll never find it!" Jacinta feels very sorry for herself and cries like a baby!

Mama reminds Jacinta of another little girl of the same name, who saw The Blessed Mother at Fatima, Portugal in 1917 - how her heart desired to *offer up* all the sacrifices she could...

Jacinta was just seven years
When she saw Our Lady's face
Even though she was quite young
Her heart held so much grace

She offered all in sacrifice
Insults, fear and pain
To bring God's love to sinner's hearts
So Heaven they might gain

At the end of the Rosary, Mama thinks of searching the little guest cottage behind the house. Jacinta has had a little change of heart and says, "It might be OK if we don't find it, so maybe I can offer it up like the other Jacinta!"

Holding hands, the two walk down the path, to the old cottage. The front door creaks open and both are surprised to see many boxes, in all shapes and sizes, for this became a storage place over the years. They wonder where to begin looking!

Suddenly, they hear a noise and bravely walk toward where the sound is coming from. Mama slowly opens a large red hat box, and there, munching on the ear of a straw-filled teddy bear, is a fat brown mouse! Jacinta finds it a bit funny at first but then she has a scary thought; There could be more mice and the veil may be half eaten by now! Mama wonders too but then tells Jacinta...

Let's be like St. Peter

Though waves crashed round his boat

He took the steps he needed

To keep his faith afloat

First one foot then the other

Over the side went he

He looked to The Lord Jesus

To calm the angry sea

So when we feel frightened

To Jesus let us say

Lord, I trust in You now

Today and every day

After a short prayer, they begin their search. They enjoy working and talking together and find many interesting things as they look among Great Grandma's belongings for the veil....

Spools of thread and balls of yarn
A hand-knit sweater too
One wooden napkin holder
And a frame of heaven-blue

A doll with curly read hair
Wearing coat and Easter bonnet
A torn and tattered choir book
With Jesus' picture on it

One dandy antique violin
Scarves with stripes and dots
A pair of wooden shoes
And gift bows made with knots

As they search, Jacinta asks her mother to tell her more about the message of Fatima and Mama is happy to share...

To three little shepherd children

Lucy, Jacinta and Francisco

Our Lady gave God's peace plan

For all the world to know

The sins of man so hurt Him

And He wants us to be pure

Penance and the Rosary

Will help mankind endure

Wear the scapular of Our Lady

Love her Immaculate Heart

Pray for it to triumph

God's plan from the start

Daddy has come in to help for a bit and says, "Mary helps us grow closer to Jesus. We should ask her to help us live the message of Fatima!"

After dinner, they open a box they brought back with them! All are filled with hope! They find books, knitting yarn, animal puzzles and cross-stitches made by Great Grandma "Dot." Suddenly, Jacinta screams, "I found it, I found it!" But it's just a fancy curtain after all! Now she is tempted once again, to see herself looking better than the others, with the treasured veil. Quietly she prays...

Oh dear Mother Mary

I have so much to learn

To know what really counts to God

To Him I want to turn

So, help me keep my heart right

And only God's Will do

This I know brings happiness

Joy and much peace too

The time has come to remove the last thing from the bottom of the box, which is a plain wooden jewelry case. Jacinta opens the little top drawer. There, she finds a sparkly crystal rosary, with a medal of Our Lady of Fatima attached! Her gloomy mood is lifted because she is happy to find the precious beads. But as she lifts it from its place, it falls apart, in three pieces! Jacinta's daddy quickly offers his help...

Have no fear my daughter

For I will fix it right

Even if it takes some time

It will be fixed tonight

The Rosary of Our Lady

Will soon be yours to pray

For those who are in need

Each and every day

Daddy tells Jacinta to go to the big storage closet, to get his tool box. She pulls a string to turn on the light. As she looks around, she sees a wooden trunk underneath a shelf with an old blanket over the top. It is marked with Great Grandmother's initials...D.E.K.

Jacinta calls out, "Mama, Daddy!" Daddy comes and pushes the trunk out of the crowded storage room to pry open the heavy lid. They are all disappointed that it seems to be full of just blankets, sheets and such. Then Mama pulls out a large flowered bag. "Unzip it and let's see what's inside," she says to Jacinta.

And behold...THE VEIL...looking brand new! Jacinta's little heart beats fast from her excitement! Her parents give her a very happy hug! Amazed at the lovely tiara, she asks about the meaning of the red stones, so Mama explains...

The stones are natural, from the earth

Red stands for Christ's own blood

They number five for His worst wounds

The bleeding lamb of God

To the cross our sins did nail Him

Who came to set us free

His hands and feet and Sacred Heart

Pierced for you and me

So let this new-found veil

Remind of holy union

He wants to give Himself to you

In each Holy Communion

Jacinta cries tears of joy, mixed with sorrow, for ever having hurt God by vanity, pride and not being thankful. Now she asks her mother's forgiveness for not seeing how lovely the dress she made for her truly is. And from her grateful heart she declares...

A miracle veil I prayed for
So all would notice me
I'm thankful for my parents
Who helped me truly see

The *miracle* is Jesus' love
His life, poured out for me
His Body, Blood and Soul
And His Divinity

I know that I am special
Not due to dress of lace
But just because He loves me
A miracle of grace

Jacinta's First Holy Communion Day arrives and she is so happy! She prays for all her friends, that they too will see how very much Jesus loves them! And...how much He wants to be loved.

THE PRAYERS OF FATIMA

THE EUCHARISTIC PRAYER

Most Holy Trinity, I adore thee. My God, my God, I love you in the most Blessed Sacrament.

SACRIFICE PRAYER

Oh my Jesus, I offer this for love of thee, for the conversion of sinners and in reparation for the sins committed against the Immaculate Heart of Mary.

DECADE PRAYER

Oh my Jesus, forgive us our sins, save us from the fires of Hell. Lead all souls to Heaven, especially those most in need of Thy mercy. Amen.

PARDON PRAYER

Oh my God, I believe, I adore, I hope and I love Thee! I beg pardon for those who do not believe, do not adore, do not hope and do not love Thee. Amen.

ANGEL'S COMMUNION PRAYER

Oh most Holy Trinity, Father, Son and Holy Spirit, I adore thee profoundly. I offer thee the most precious Body, Blood, Soul and Divinity of Jesus Christ, present in all the tabernacles of the world. In reparation for the outrages, sacrileges and indifference by which He is offended. By the infinite merits of

the Sacred Heart of Jesus and the Immaculate Heart of Mary, I beg the conversion of poor sinners. Amen.

About The Author and Artist - Nellie Edwards
And the story behind "Jacinta's Miracle Veil"

Nellie was raised in a large Catholic family and grew to love The Blessed Virgin Mary at a very young age. She is the mother of eight children and twenty five grand-blessings and wants to help them and many more children learn about the message and miracle of Fatima. She likes to share that it is through talking to God in prayer, especially the Rosary, that it becomes easier to do what He asks of us...

One day she painted the face of a little girl and thought of putting a Communion dress and veil on her. Then suddenly she knew she had to write "Jacinta's Miracle Veil!" She knew that God inspired the idea but she had never done artwork for a children's book, so she prayed and asked Him to help her. Do you think He did? She hopes you will learn the *prayers of Fatima* and its message, so you can do God's Will always. May all your Communions be as your First - full of love for Jesus, just like it was for little "Jacinta."

You can learn more about the Message of Fatima when you visit

Fatima Family Apostolate; An Association of Pontifical Rite

www.FatimaFamily.org

Look for the Companion Book, "Francisco's Miracle Lamb"
Visit Nellie's Website: www.PaintedFaith.Net

May The Body of Christ bring us to everlasting Life.
AMEN

My First Communion Photo

My Prayer of Thanks to Jesus

Dear Jesus,

Thank you for coming to me today in First Holy Communion. You have given me the most important gift possible in this life...Your very Body, Blood, Soul and Divinity...Your REAL Presence! I will try my best to always remember that this is a great miracle every time I come to receive You. Help me to live always to please you, by staying close to You in prayer, by obedience to my parents and to never miss Mass, where You bring Heaven to Earth.

With my whole heart and soul,

_____

Date of my 1st Holy communion_____

My Pastor's Name_____

Name of my Parish_____